Visit us on the Web!
randomhouse.com/kids
Kohls.com/Kids

Educators and librarians, for a variety of teaching tools, visit us at
RHTeachersLibrarians.com

This special edition was printed for Kohl's Department Stores, Inc.
(for distribution on behalf of Kohl's Cares, LLC, its wholly owned subsidiary),
by Random House Children's Books, New York.

Kohl's
5026216-00
123386
09/13–02/14

MANUFACTURED IN CHINA

10 9 8 7 6 5 4 3 2 1

The NOSE BOOK

By **Al Perkins**
Illustrated by **Joe Mathieu**

BEGINNER BOOKS®
A Division of Random House, Inc.

Everybody
grows
a nose.

I see a nose
on every face.

I see noses
every place!

A nose
between
each pair of eyes.

Noses!
Noses!
Every size.

They grow
on every
kind of head.

They come in blue . . .
. . . and pink
. . . and red.

Some are
very, very long.

Some are
very, very strong.

Everywhere a fellow goes,
he sees some
new, new kind of nose.

A nose is useful.
After all . . .
some play horns . . .

. . . and some play ball.

A nose is good
for making holes
. . . in trees

. . . and roofs

. . . and barber poles.

But sometimes
noses aren't much fun.
They sniffle.

They get burned by sun.

A nose gets punched . . .

. . . and bumped on doors

. . . and bumped on walls

. . . and bumped on floors!

Sometimes
your nose
will make you sad.
Sometimes
your nose
will make you mad.
BUT . . .

Just suppose
you had no nose!
Then you
could never
smell
a rose . . .

. . . or pie, or chicken à la king.

You'd never smell a single thing.

And one thing more.
Suppose . . . no nose . . .

Where would
all our glasses sit?
They'd all fall off!
Just THINK of it!

And that's why
everybody grows,
between his eyes,
some kind of nose!